Exclusive distributors:
Music Sales Limited
8/9 Frith Street,
London W1V 5TZ,
England.
Music Sales Pty Limited
120 Rothschild Avenue,
Rosebery, NSW 2018,
Australia.

This book © Copyright 1990 by
Wise Publications
Order No.AM77967
ISBN 0.7119.2110.5

Bee Gees
The Anthology

Compiled by Peter Evans

Cover design by
Pearce Marchbank Studio

Cover photographs courtesy of
London Features International

Music Sales' complete catalogue lists thousands of titles
and is free from your local music shop, or direct from
Music Sales Limited. Please send £1 in stamps for postage to
Music Sales Limited, 8/9 Frith Street, London W1V 5TZ.

Printed in the United Kingdom by
Dotesios Printers Limited, Trowbridge, Wiltshire.

Wise Publications
London/New York/Sydney

Morning Of My Life (In The Morning)

Words & Music by Barry Gibb

morning of my life The

minutes take so long to drift away Please be

patient with your life It's only morning and you've

still to live your day. In the evening

New York Mining Disaster 1941

Words & Music by Barry Gibb & Robin Gibb

8

Jones? Do you know what it's like on the out - side? Don't go

talk - ing too loud, you'll cause a land - slide, Mis - ter Jones.

I keep strain - ing my ears to hear a sound; may - be

some - one is dig - ging un - der - ground. Or have they giv - en up and all gone home to

To Love Somebody

Words & Music by Barry Gibb & Robin Gibb

Holiday

Words & Music by Barry Gibb & Robin Gibb

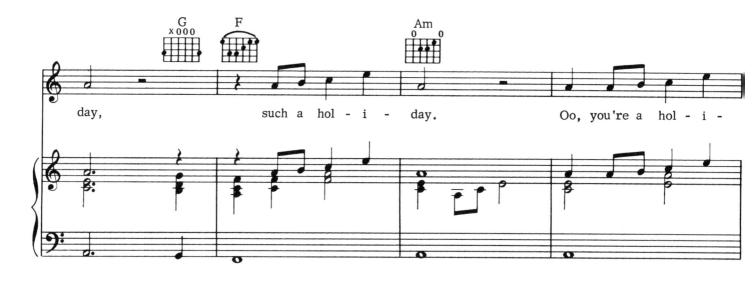

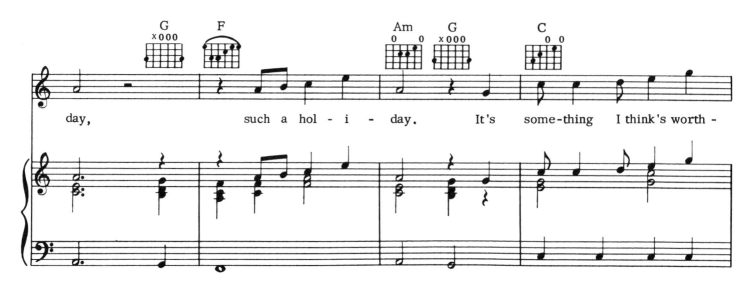

while,　　　　if the pup - pet makes you smile;　　　　if

not, then you're throw-ing stones, throw-ing stones,— throw-ing stones.—

Oo, it's a fun - ny game; don't be - lieve that it's all the same.
Oo, you're a hol - i - day, ev - 'ry day such a hol - i - day.

Can't think what I've just said; put the soft pil - low on my head.
Now it's my turn to say, and I say you're a hol - i - day. It's

World

Words & Music by Barry Gibb, Robin Gibb & Maurice Gibb

Massachusetts

Words & Music by Barry Gibb, Robin Gibb & Maurice Gibb

home._ And the lights all went out in Mas - sa -
do. __ And the lights all went out in Mas - sa -
seen._ And the lights all went out in Mas - sa -

chu - setts the day I left her
chu - setts; they brought me back to
chu - setts; and Mas - sa - chu - setts is

stand - ing on her own.
see my way with you.
one place I have seen.

I will re - mem - ber Mas - sa - chu - setts.

Repeat and fade

I've Got To Get A Message To You

Words & Music by Barry Gibb, Robin Gibb & Maurice Gibb

once in your life_ you're a - lone,_____ but you ain't got a dime,_ there's no
once in my life_ I'm a - lone,_____ and I got - ta let her know just in
cry-ing, but deep_ down in - side,_____ well, I did it to him,__ now it's

time for the phone." I've just got - ta get a mes-sage to you;_
time be - fore I go.
my turn to die._

hold on,_____ hold on._____ One more hour and my life will be through;_

hold on,_____ hold on. ____ { Well, I _____ I've just

Idea

Words & Music by Barry Gibb, Robin Gibb & Maurice Gibb

25

I Started A Joke

Words & Music by Barry Gibb, Robin Gibb & Maurice Gibb

see ... that the joke was on

me, ... oh, _____ no. _____

I start - ed to cry
I fi - nal - ly died ... which start - ed the whole world
... which start - ed the whole world

laugh - ing; }
liv - ing; } ... oh, if I'd on - ly

Odessa

Words & Music by Barry Gibb, Maurice Gibb & Robin Gibb

Moderately slow

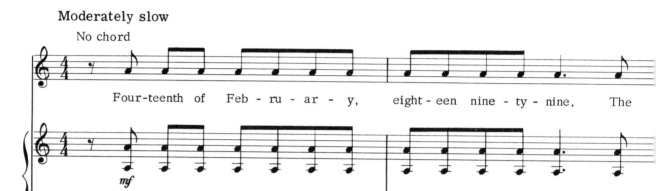

Four-teenth of Feb-ru-ar-y, eight-een nine-ty-nine. The

Brit-ish ship Ve-ron-i-ca was lost with-out a sign. Baa baa black sheep, you

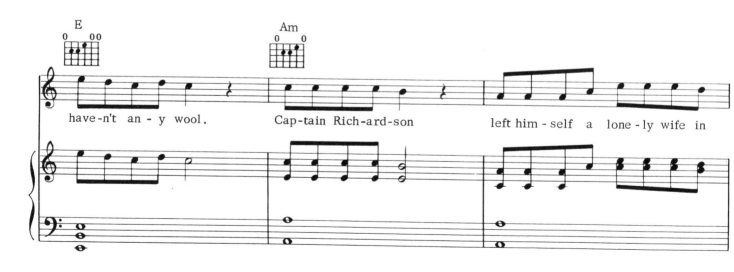

have-n't an-y wool. Cap-tain Rich-ard-son left him-self a lone-ly wife in

Hull.

Slightly faster

Cher - ub,___ I lost a ship___ in the Bal - tic sea.___
Treas - ure,___ you know the neigh - bours that lived___ next door.___

I'm on an ice - berg run - ning free.___
They have-n't got___ their dog an - y - more.

I? _____ O - des - sa. _____

How time goes by. _____

Tempo I
N.C.

Four-teenth of Feb-ru-ar-y, eight-een nine-ty-nine. The

Brit-ish ship Ve-ron-i-ca was lost with-out a sign.

And The Sun Will Shine

Words & Music by Barry Gibb, Maurice Gibb & Robin Gibb

First Of May

Words & Music by Barry Gibb, Maurice Gibb & Robin Gibb

39

Words

Words & Music by Barry Gibb, Robin Gibb & Maurice Gibb

Talk in ev-er-last-ing words and ded-i-cate them all to me.

And I will give you all my life, I'm here if you should

call to me. You think that I don't e-ven

mean a sin-gle word I say. It's on-ly

Tacet

42

words, and words are all I have to take your heart a -

way. It's on - ly words, and words are all I

have to take your heart a - way. It's on - ly

words, and words are all I have to take your heart a - way.

rit.

mp

I.O.I.O

Words & Music by Barry Gibb & Maurice Gibb

All the morn - ing birds — that sing ___ a - bove ___ still
Now my morn - ings are ___ for won - d'ring ___ and my

bring back mem - o - ries ___ of a girl ___ who stood be - side ___
nights to rea - son why ___ why a stran - ger comes to steal ___

___ me the love ___ when the rights I did were wrong. _____
___ me the love ___ of a girl I had to hold. _____

But she went ___ back down ___ the riv - er just when I

Don't Forget To Remember

Words & Music by Barry Gibb & Maurice Gibb

get o - ver an - y - thing __ you want, _____ my
mir - ror of my soul, so take __ me out _____ of my

love, but I can't get my - self o - ver
hole. Let me try _____ to go on liv - in' _____ right __

you.
now. }
Don't for - get to re - mem - ber me

and the love that used to be. I still re - mem - ber you.

Lonely Days

Words & Music by Barry Gibb, Maurice Gibb & Robin Gibb

If I Can't Have You

Words & Music by Barry Gibb, Maurice Gibb & Robin Gibb

Nights On Broadway

Words & Music by Barry Gibb, Robin Gibb & Maurice Gibb

Moderately slow (in 2), with a strong beat

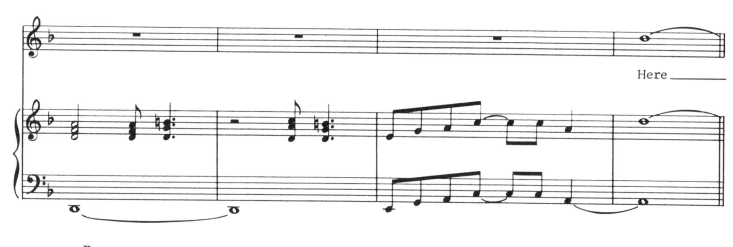

Here

we are in a room full of
in my place there are so man-y

Run To Me

Words & Music by Barry Gibb, Maurice Gibb & Robin Gibb

Moderately slow, with a beat

If ev - er you've got

rain in your_ heart,_ some -one has hurt_ you _ and
out in the _ cold, _ no one be - side_ you _ and

torn _ you _ a - part. _ Am I _ un - wise _ to
no _ one _ to hold. _ Am I _ un - wise _ to

o-pen up your eyes to love me, and let it be like they said it would be,
o-pen up your eyes to love me, and when you've got noth-ing to lose,

me lov-ing you girl and you lov-ing me.
noth-ing to pay for and noth-ing to choose,

Am I un-wise to o-pen up your eyes to love
Am I un-wise to o-pen up your eyes to love

Chorus

Run to me when-ev-er you're lone-ly, run to me if you need a shoul-der.
(me.)

How Can You Mend A Broken Heart

Words & Music by Barry Gibb & Robin Gibb

Wind Of Change

Words & Music by Barry Gibb & Robin Gibb

In the streets of New York Cit - y ev-'ry man

Don't you un-der-stand what I'm say - in', we need

——— can feel the cold.

——— a god down here.

And I don't want no pit -

A man to lead us chil -

Jive Talkin'

Words & Music by Barry Gibb, Robin Gibb & Maurice Gibb

Moderately, with a strong beat

You Should Be Dancing

Words & Music by Barry Gibb, Robin Gibb & Maurice Gibb

Moderately, with a beat

My ba-by moves at mid-night, goes
juic-y and she's trou-ble, she

right on till the dawn; my wom-an takes me high - er,
gets it to me good; my wom-an gives me pow - er,

Love So Right

Words & Music by Barry Gibb, Robin Gibb & Maurice Gibb

84

How Deep Is Your Love

Words & Music by Barry Gibb, Robin Gibb & Maurice Gibb

More Than A Woman

Words & Music by Barry Gibb, Robin Gibb & Maurice Gibb

Medium Disco beat

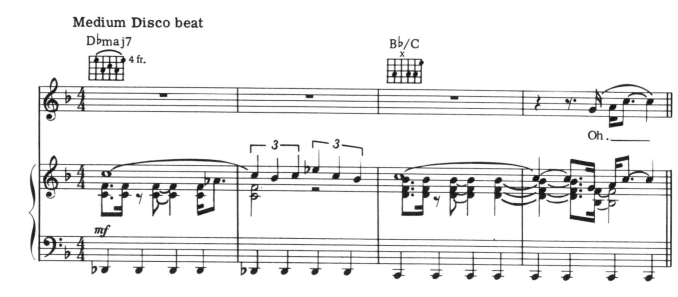

Oh.

Girl, I've known you ver - y well. I've seen you grow-in' ev - 'ry day.__ I nev-

There are sto - ries old__ and true of peo - ple so__ in love__ like you__ and me,

er real - ly looked__ be - fore,__ but now you take my breath a - way.__

__ and I__ can see__ my - self__ let his - to - ry re - peat it - self.__ Re-

Night Fever

Words & Music by Barry Gibb, Robin Gibb & Maurice Gibb

reach out for me,___ yeah, and the feel-in' is___ bright, then I get

night fe-ver, night fe-ver._____ We know how to do___

___ it. Gim-me that

night fe-ver, night fe-ver._____ We know how to show___

94

Stayin' Alive

Words & Music by Barry Gibb, Robin Gibb & Maurice Gibb

all right.__ It's O K.__ And you may look__ the oth - er way.__
all right.__ It's O K.__ I'll live to see__ an - oth - er day.__

We can try__ to un - der - stand__ the New York Times' ef - fect__ on man.__

Wheth - er you're a broth - er or wheth - er you're a moth - er, you're stay - in' a - live,__ stay - in' a - live.__

Feel the cit - y break - in' and ev - 'ry - bod - y shak - in', and we're stay - in' a - live,__ stay - in' a - live.__

Some-bod-y help me. ___   Some-bod-y help_ me, yeah. ___

Fm7   Bb7

Life go-in' no-where. ___

Fm7

Some-bod-y help_ me, yeah. ___   I'm stay-in' a-live. ___

E.S.P.

Words & Music by Barry Gibb, Maurice Gibb & Robin Gibb

Angela

Words & Music by Barry Gibb, Robin Gibb & Maurice Gibb

108

You Win Again

Words & Music by Barry Gibb, Robin Gibb & Maurice Gibb

I could-n't fig – ure why you could-n't give me what ev – 'ry-bod-y___ needs___ Should-n't let you

kick me when I'm down my ba – by Find out ev – 'ry-bod-y knows that you've been us-ing me

I'm sur – – prised you let me stay a – round you One day I'm gonn-a

111

Ordinary Lives

Words & Music by Barry Gibb, Robin Gibb & Maurice Gibb

There'll be one small light ___ all ov - er the world ___ to - night.___

VERSE 2:
Say goodbye cruel world
No pity no pain tonight
Whatever the cost all is lost
If this is love with no name
Then it's all in the stars
Whether it's wrong or right
There's no one to blame no lies
What else could we do
Living ordinary lives
Made a dream for you
Living ordinary lives.

One

Words & Music by Barry Gibb, Robin Gibb & Maurice Gibb

al - ways, __ bright-er than the eye can see, we hide the sun. __

1. The taste of love is sweet-er like hon-ey on __ the vine, like the wind that feeds __ the fi - re, two __ souls be-come en-twined. Some - day __ ba - by you and I should be one, __ one. __ (2.) So I'm

VERSE 2:

So I'm standing 'round this corner
Tall enough to touch the New York sky, oh yes
My love is so blind
I just cannot hear or see the world go by, oh yes
Someone can love so completely
One kiss should break the seal
Truth can be stronger than fiction
This love is real
This love is real.

VERSE 3:

I will follow
Count on me, I'll never let you down, oh yes
My devotion
If love is an ocean I'll surely drown, oh yes
You'll be my only possession
I'll be a slave to you
We hold the power together
Just me and you
Just me and you.

Wish You Were Here

Words & Music by Barry Gibb, Robin Gibb & Maurice Gibb

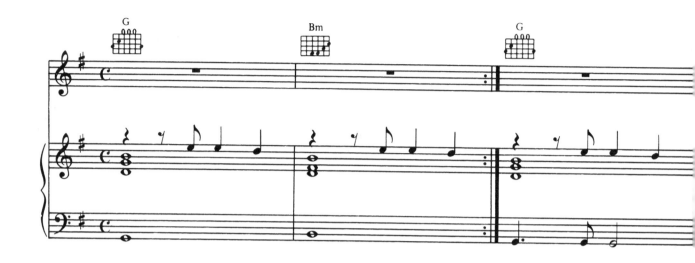

You're

liv-ing your life___ in some-bo-dy el - se's heart. ___

VERSE 2:
And so I awake
In somebody else's dream
(It's not what it seems)
It's only a lie
I've yet to decide who's real.

The blood red rose will never never die
It'll burn like a flame
In the dark of the night
I'm not afraid
I'd give everything
If you hear me there.

CHORUS 2:
Ahh
I wish you were here
Drying these tears I cry
They were good times
It's that time of year
For being alone
But you're dealing with a heart of stone
Try to kiss and say goodbye
Try to throw our love away
And that storm will blow.

D.S.
'Cause you're dealing with a heart of stone
Try to kiss and say goodbye
Try to throw our love away
And I can't let go.